Fairy Puzzles

Stella Maidment and Daniela Dogliani

QED Publishing

If you get stuck, the answers are at the back of the book!

Editor: Alexandra Koken
Designer: Elaine Wilkinson

First published in the UK in 2012 by
QED Publishing
A Quarto Group company
230 City Road
London EC1V 2TT

www.qed-publishing.co.uk

A catalogue record for this book is available from the British Library.

ISBN 978 1 84835 864 5

Printed in China

Welcome to Fairyland!
This is Flora the fairy.
And this is her little brother, Eddie the elf.
Solve the puzzles in this book and help Flora organize the Midsummer Party!
Look out for Buzz the bee too. You'll find him in every picture!

Flora has a special visitor.
It's the fairy queen!

Can you spot these things?

three butterflies

a watering can

a worm

Can you help the fairy queen find Flora?

"I want you to organize our Midsummer Party," says the queen.

Can you spot these things?

a golden crown

a snail

three yellow flowers

Which of the queen's horses is
different from the others?

Flora is very excited! She starts by making some invitations.

Each invitation has a matching envelope. Match them up!

Can you spot these things?

pink fairy dust

scissors

two paintbrushes

Eddie and the birds help Flora to deliver the invitations.

Fern

Buttercup

Can you spot these things?

a dandelion

three strawberries

two ladybirds

Which fairy gets
which invitation?
Blossom
Elvira

Flora asks the Elf Orchestra
to play at the party.

Can you find the outlines of three guitars hidden in the picture?

Can you spot these things?

two spiders

a beetle

a lunchbox

On the day of the party, Flora makes garlands to decorate the fairy circle.

Which two garlands are the same?

Can you spot these things?

a mole

a mouse

two caterpillars

Eddie hangs lanterns from the trees.
Can you find three pink lanterns?

Can you spot these things?

a bird's nest

two spider's webs

a dragonfly

There are lots of
berries and cupcakes
to eat.

Which plate of cakes is different from the other two?

Can you spot these things?

a jug

a jelly

three spoons

"Now I need a party dress," says Flora, waving her magic wand.

Flora chooses a pink dress with white flowers on the skirt. Which one is it?

Can you spot these things?

two necklaces

a pair of yellow shoes

a feather

At dusk, the guests start to arrive.

Can you help them find their way to the party?

Can you spot these things?

an owl

a fairy in a green cape

a cottage

All the fairies dance until dawn.

Can you find the fairy twins?

Can you spot these things?
three stars
a trumpet
a fairy handbag

The fairy queen thanks Flora for a wonderful party and gives her a special present.

Can you guess what it is?

Can you spot these things?

the fairy queen's carriage

a present for Eddie

a teddy bear

Answers

Pages 4-5

Follow the red line to help the fairy queen find Flora.

Pages 6-7

The horse circled in red has a different mane.

Pages 8-9

The blue lines show which cards match the envelopes.

Pages 10-11

Follow the colourful lines to match the fairies and envelopes.

Pages 12-13

The hidden guitar outlines are circled in red.

Pages 14-15

The matching garlands are circled in red.

Pages 16-17

The three pink lanterns are circled in red.

Pages 18-19

The plate on the left is different:
Eddie has taken one of the cupcakes!

Answers

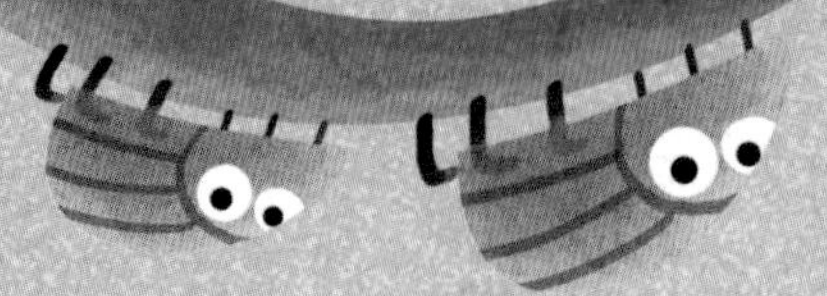

Pages 20-21

Flora's dress is circled in red.

Pages 22-23

The red line leads to the party.

Pages 24-25

The fairy twins are circled in red.

Pages 26-27

Flora is given a brand new wand!

More fairy fun

Fairy day!

Dress up as a fairy for the day. Wear a pretty dress and put flowers in your hair. Make a magic wand out of a cardboard star and a wooden spoon. Choose a special fairy name like Cobweb, Bluebell or Blossom. You could even host a fairy-themed party!

A fairy picnic

Fill a little picnic basket with tiny foods like little gem biscuits. If you have a doll's tea set you could use this too. Take your picnic into the garden or to a local park and put a picnic rug under a shady tree. Or you could stay indoors and make a secret picnic area!

Rainbow tangle

You'll need different-coloured balls of wool or string. Tie the end of one ball around a table leg then unravel the string, draping it over and under furniture. Tie the end of the string around a small treat and hide it out of sight. Do the same with the other balls of string, criss-crossing them to make a tangle. Then untie the ends from the table and give each person a different string to follow.

Fairy chains

Fold a piece of paper accordion-style (pleated). Draw a fairy shape on the top layer, making sure the fairy's arms extend to the edges. Cut around the outline and unfold your chain of little fairies holding hands! Decorate as you wish.